Tree-House Comix Proudly Presents

DOG MAN

A Tale of Two Kitties

WRITTEN AND ILLUSTRATED BY **DAV PILKEY**

AS GEORGE BEARD AND HAROLD HUTCHINS

WITH COLOR BY JOSE GARIBALDI

graphix

AN IMPRINT OF

SCHOLASTIC

HERE'S TO YOU, MR. ROBINSON! (THANK YOU, DICK.)

Library of Congress Control Number 2016961907

ISBN 978-0-545-93521-0

10 9 8 7 6 5 4 3 2 1   17 18 19 20 21

Printed in China   62
First edition, September 2017

Edited by Anamika Bhatnagar
Book design by Dav Pilkey and Phil Falco
Color by Jose Garibaldi
Creative Director: David Saylor

ChapTers

DOG MAN

Behind the scenes

Hi, everybody. It's your old pals, George and Harold.

Yo, what up, dogs?

We're in 5th grade now. We're older and wiser...

... and Totally mature, I might add.

We even got a new teacher named Ms. Chivess. She's Pretty cool...

... except for one thing. She makes us read <u>classic Literature.</u>

This month we're reading <u>A Tale of two cities.</u>

And we're having a dickens of a time!!!

HA HA HA HA HA HA HA HA HA

Like we said, we're totally mature now.

Anyway, we didn't think we'd like it, but it's actually pretty good.

A Tale of two cities charles Dickens

Yeah. It's <u>deep</u> and <u>stuff.</u>

...a Tale of
redemption...

A Tale of
oppression...

And So...
Tree House
comix
Proudly
Presents:

Now We're Deep, Too!

It inspired us to make a brand
new Dog Man graphic novel!

But First...

...a recap of our story thus far:

A TALE of Two Kitties

...a tale of rebirth...

...and a tale of hope.

They were the worst of cops.

They were the best of cops...

Supa Recap!

DOG MAN

There was a cop with a dog's head on the cold streets of a savage city...

...There was a cat with a wicked heart enchained in kitty custody.

Rats!

Cat Jail

And so begins our tale of mirth and woe.

It ain't easy being deep and mature...

... but somebody's gotta do it!

OH Boy, this is gonna be Great!

Hey, Everybody!!!

COPS

We're in the News!

And it's a **GOOD** story this time!

Look!

Trending News
DoG Man and ChieF are Heroes!
By Sarah Hatoff

How Many Times have we TALKED About This?

That's **No Way** For a cop To behave!

I'm gettin' **TiRed** of This !!

Tired, Tired, **TiRED!**

Hey, Chief. Didn't you want to Show Dog Man the news?

Oh, Yeah!

LOOK! WE'RE HEROES...

...because we saved the world from FLIPPY!!!

Lick Lick Lick

EVIL GENIUS FISH THWARTED

It says here that scientists are going to study FLIPPY's brain!

DOG MAN, I have an important job for you!

I'm putting you in charge of security!

Who wants to protect the scientists?

Look, Petey!

Petey!

Hey, Petey!

and here's one for you, Mr. Whiskers. Respect!

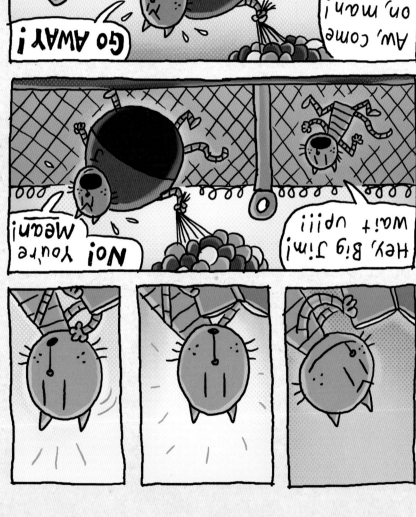

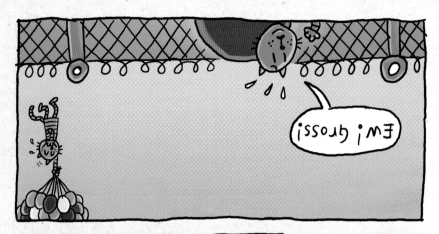

Home at Last!

Hmmmm...

...and has a wretched soul. Like me!!!

Someone who thinks like me and acts like me...

I need to get a new butler!!!!

Boy, this place is a dump!

Keep OUT! Lab Sweet Lab

"Ding-Dong!"

Gimme! Gimme!

Cloning Machine

add to cart

click

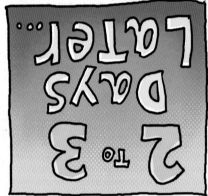

2 To 3 Days Later...

And So.... Tik Tak Tik Tak

I've Got it!

Step 1: Insert DNA into DNA Chute.

OW!

SLAM!

please sign here...

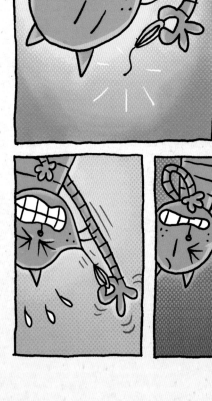

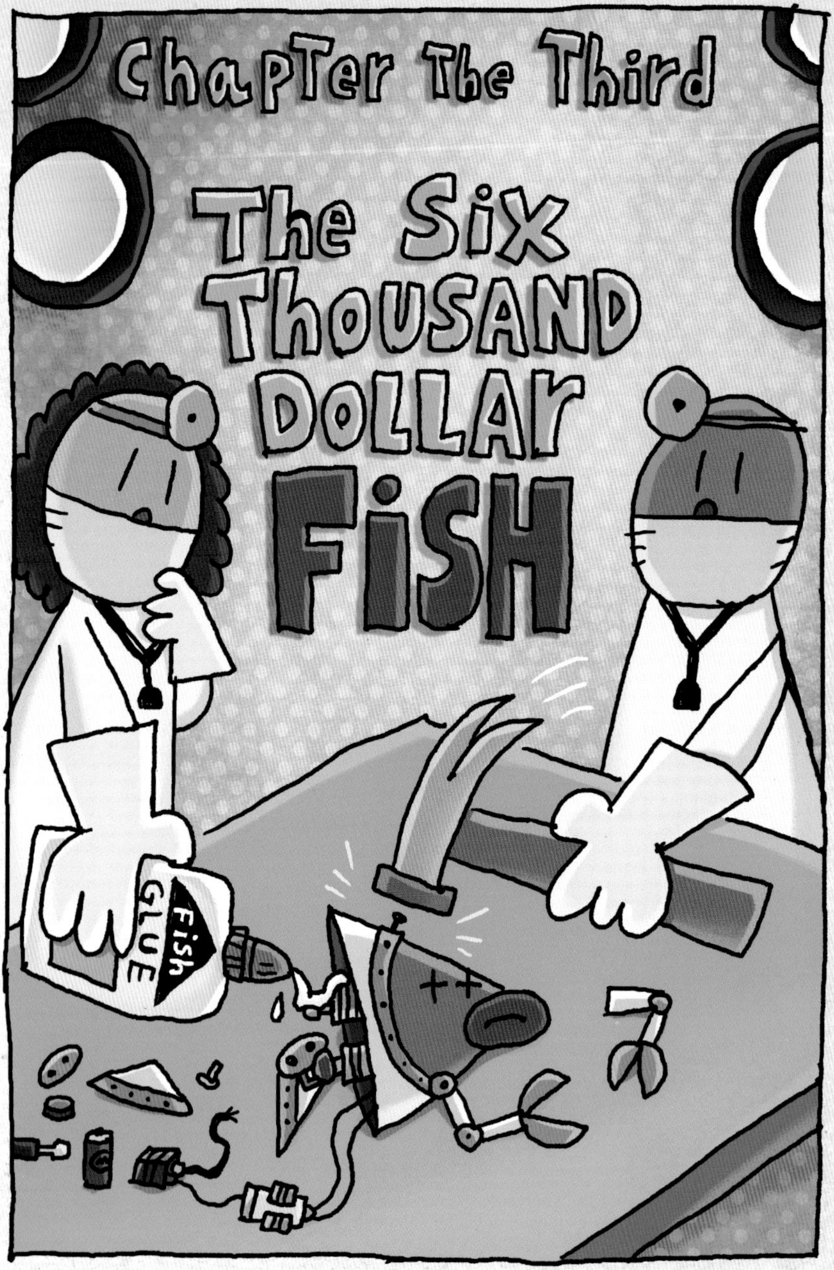
Chapter The Third
The Six Thousand Dollar Fish
Fish GLUE

HeLLo, I'm Dr. Dookie from "The Supa Awesome Science Center over There".

Our Team of Science dudes just returned from the mountain.

We went there to dig up FLippy the Psychokinetic Fish.

Why'd ya dig him up?

'Cuz we wanna study his amazing brain. D_uh_!

But I thought FLippy was dead!!!

He is!

But fortunately, he was perfectly preserved in ice.

Show 'em, DOG Man!

See? Not a scratch on him!

What wonders can FLippy's brain teach us?

STEP 1.
First, place your left hand inside the dotted lines marked "Left hand here". Hold the book open FLAT!

STEP 2:
Grasp the right-hand page with your thumb and index finger (inside the dotted lines marked "Right Thumb Here").

STEP 3:
Now QUICKLY flip the right-hand page back and forth until the picture appears to be Animated.

(for extra fun, try adding your own sound-effects!)

.RAMA

Remember,

while you are flipping,
be sure you can see
The image on page **43**
AND the image on page **45.**

If you flip quickly,
the two pictures will
start to look like
one **Animated** cartoon!

Don't forget to
add your own
sound-effects!

Left
hand here.

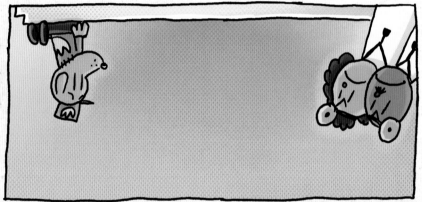

Soon, the scientists had a big operation.

They replaced all of Flippy's broken bones...

...with bionics!

Flippy was now more machine than fish.

Boy, it's a good thing Flippy is dead!

I know! He'd be _so_ Dangerous if he ever came back to Life!!!

Yeah--- with his telekinetic brain AND bionic super strength? He'd be **unSToppable**!!!

Well, I'm glad we don't have to worry about that!

Me too! With Dog Man guarding him, what could go wrong?

Let's go home and get some rest!

good idea!

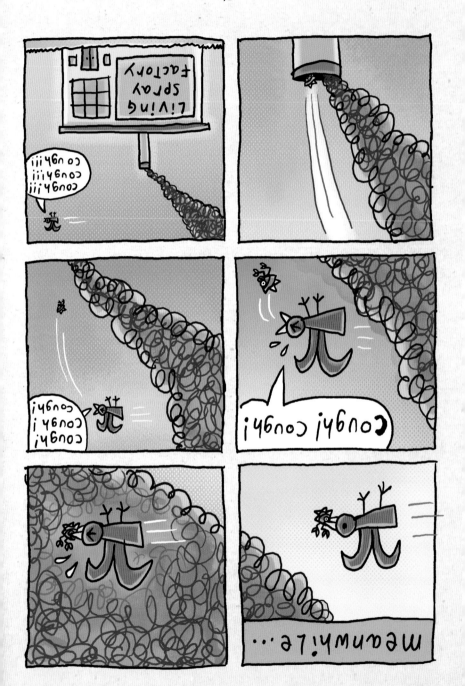

Chapter The Fourth

No More Kitten Around!

Did you fall down?

CRASH!

Oh, boy! New test Tubes!!!

09

It's about time!!!

Soon...

Why don't you go make me a cup of tea instead!

OK

Look! I made you a book!

Hey Papa!

Later...

PSSSSP

Hey! This is Pretty Good!

Thanks. I couldn't find the tea strainer...

... So I used the fly swatter!

THAT DOES IT!

He doesn't have a name!

I do too have a name! My name's "Li'L Petey."

Heh-heh. Don't Listen to him.

You can call him whatever you want!

I think I'll call you "Snowball"!!!

I Think I'LL call you "Poo-Poo head".

Gee **Whiz!** What is **WRONG** with everybody these days?

It makes ya worry about the future!

"Duh, how much does he cost?"

WHAT AN IDIOT!!

I mean, The sign **CLEARLY** says...

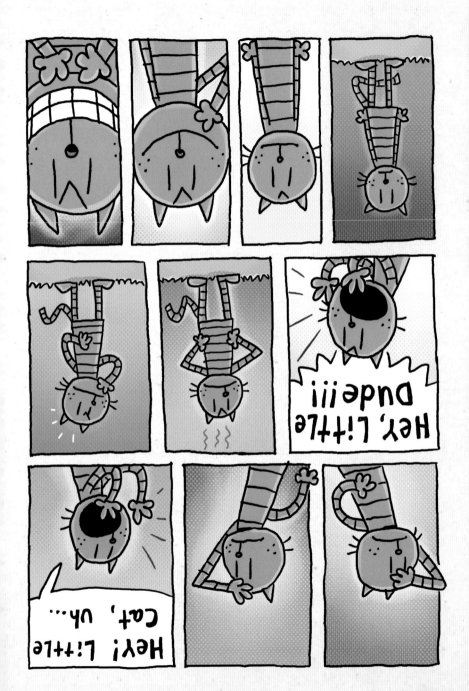

...We are all
alone tonight...

...filled with
sad uncertainty...

Life is hard
and filled with
fright...

...for my little
crate and me...

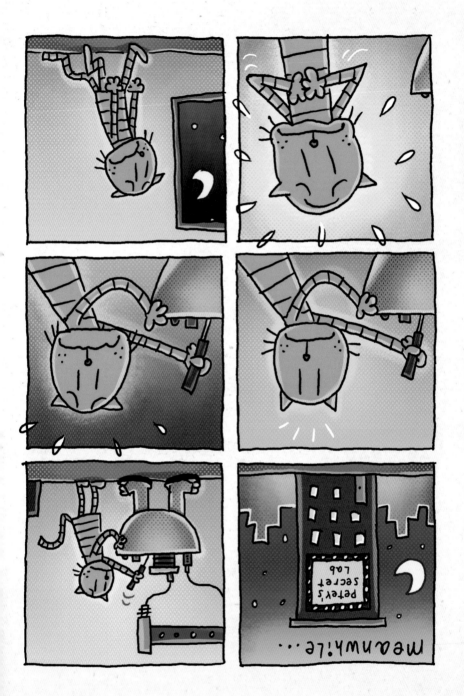

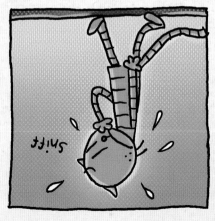

Papa
and me
go to
our car

Look at
Papa's
new
invention

Papa
and me
think
the same
things.

Smokestack
Filter

Hey, what's this?!!?

I'm not sure. It Looks Like some sort of evil, bionic, Psychokinetic, dead fish!

But how did it get stuck in our Smoke-stack?

And who could be responsible for such a thing?

Awww, Look!

Ruff! Ruff! Ruff! Ruff! Ruff!

GRRRRRRRRR

Right Thumb here.

401

KISS
KISS
KISS

Jump
Jump
Jump

BRUSH
BRUSH
BRUSH

Tree-
House
comix
Proudly
Presents

Chapter . The Sixth

A BUNCHA STUFF THAT HAPPENED Next!

FLIP FLOP FLIP FLOP FLIP

BY GEORGE AND Harold

Meanwhile...

Peter's
Secret
Lab

And so...

chunka chunka chunka

Now go find the kid who made it!

Ok, bub. I need you to scan this comic.

Don't call me Papa!!!

Hey, where's Dog Man?!

Oh, hi, Papa.

And so....

Petey's Secret Lab

Flip flop it

FLIP FLOP FLIP FLOP!

flip flop

Hey, Look! It's DOG MAN!!!!

Watch and Learn, Kid!!!!

RUFF!

RUFF RUFF

OH! Look who's here! It's Petey!!!

Look at me! I'm sooo smart! I'm totally cool!

I build Awesome robots and other cool stuff!!!!

I'm gonna Rule the world one day!

Chapter the Seventh
Recalled to Life

Can he play duck-duck-goose?

Yeah, but--- **NO!!!** Why would you want to---

Listen, kid: **YOU'RE MY CLONE!!!**

That means **YOU** are the **SAME** as **ME!**

Your soul is wretched just like mine!

You've got a whole lifetime of evilness ahead of you!

WHAT PART of "EVIL ROBOT"...

...DO YOU **NOT** UNDERSTAND?!!?

Petey's Secret Lab

Meanwhile...

Living Spray Factory

HAW HAW HAW!!!

This "Living Spray Gas" has brought me back to Life!

And it Looks Like I've got a few improvements!!!

138

But supa Mecha Flippy was not the **ONLY** thing coming to Life.

As the Living Spray gas Spread throughout the Factory...

EXIT

...the Factory began coming to Life, Too!

GOOBA GABA!

Living Spray factory

This **BEASTY BUILDING** is just what I need to help me get **REVENGE!!!**

Soon, the Living Spray Factory ran out of gas...

Uh-oh.

...but not before it had created a whole army of **Beasty Buildings!**

Haw Haw Haw!!! And I'm controlling them all with my supa mind powers!!!

Left hand here.

Right Thumb here.

Rock-a-Bye Papa

Disco Papa

Petting Papa

Hey Gang! A buncha buildings came to Life, and they're about to attack!

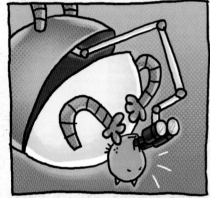

Wow! Binoculars!

ka-click

Zummmmm

Petey

I wish I could see Better!

We're supposed to be the BAD GUYS!!!

COME BACK!

Li'l Petey!

Lab

Chapter the Eighth
THE French Dressing Revolution
French
SALAD
Dressing

Hey Chief, Let's help Dog Man and Zuzu destroy some more buildings!

Ok!

MY BEAUTIFUL BEASTY Buildings!

WHO COULD HAVE DONE Such a Thing???

Hey! what happened over Here?

Oh, No! Dog Man and ZuZu just ran out of Salad dressing!

But that's not the worst of their problems!

LOOK OUT, DOG MAN AND ZUZU!

French SALAD Dressing

It looked
like this
was the
end...

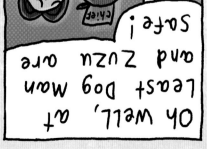

Right
Thumb
here.
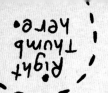

He takes a lickin'
and keeps on tickin'!!!

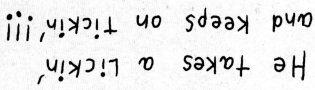

He takes a lickin'
and keeps on tickin'!!!

...but it didn't last long!

GOOBA GABA!

GOOBA GABA!

GOOBA GABA!

GOOBA GABA!

It was a Happy reunion...

Right Thumb Here.

And so...

WHUMP

HOORAY!!!

Those Jerks may have defeated my Beasty Buildings...

...but they're no match for my psychokinetic mind powers!!!

I think I'll start by getting rid of this Robo-Cat!

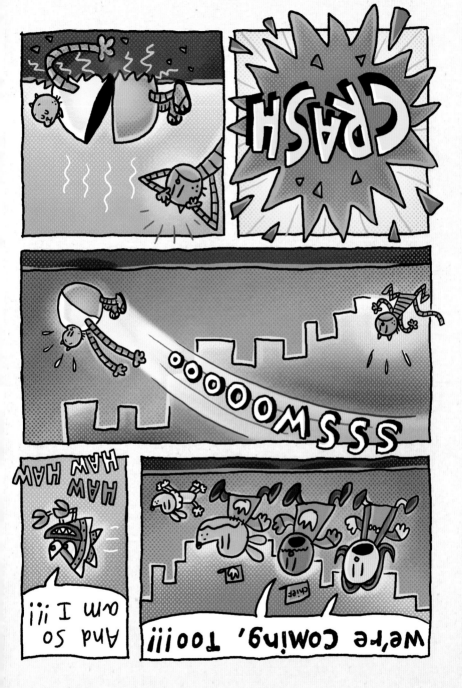

Meanwhile, it looked like the gang had escaped.

Hey, it's my cop car!

Let's hide out in this building.

Ok!

ART SUPPLIES

Hurry!

And soon...

Meanwhile...

Hmmm... How should I get rid of this guy?

I know! I'LL drop him into that volcano over there!!!

And once he is gone...

...I'LL destroy Dog Man and his "heroic" friends!!!

Meanwhile...

...Things were not looking very good for Petey. He was being lifted higher and higher by the mighty brain powers of Supa Mecha Flippy.

HAW HAW HAW!

As soon as he reaches 10,000 feet, I'LL drop him into that volcano!

But then...

SCREECH

HEY! WATCH where you're driving, Lead-Foot!!!

Hi, FLiPPy. What'cha doing?

I'm very busy destroying This Robo-cat!

why?

'cuz he's a **Jerk!**

why?

FLIPPY and me FLEW UP To a star.

they had a swing set so we swinged on it.

I FELL off BUT FLiPPY saved me.

This was not good news for Petey.

Uh-Oh!

YAAAAAA

Oh well...

...I guess this is the end.

GOOD-BYE, CRUEL WORLD!

It is a far, far better...

...Rest that I go to...

...than I have ever known!

by George and Harold

Three Endings

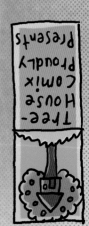

Tree-House Comix Proudly Presents

Chapter the Tenth

Flippy, you've been a naughty fish today!

I know.

But then...

Zuzu and I are making a citizen's arrest!

OK.

Soon, everyone was safely on the ground.

HOORAY FOR DOG MAN!

Phooey!

chief

The First Ending

FLiPPY'S STORY

Yeah... Well...

I may be weak...

Li'l Petey
c/o Dog Man's House
over by that one tree
U.S.A.

To: FLippY
c/o Fish JaiL
U.S.A.

...and I may be rusty...

FLippY
and me
meet
Mr. Bug

FLippY
and me
meet
Mr. Bug

...but I'm happy!

to
FLippY

I Like
FLippY

fun

FLippY
Time

SUPA
FLippY

FLippY
and me
meet
Mr. Bug

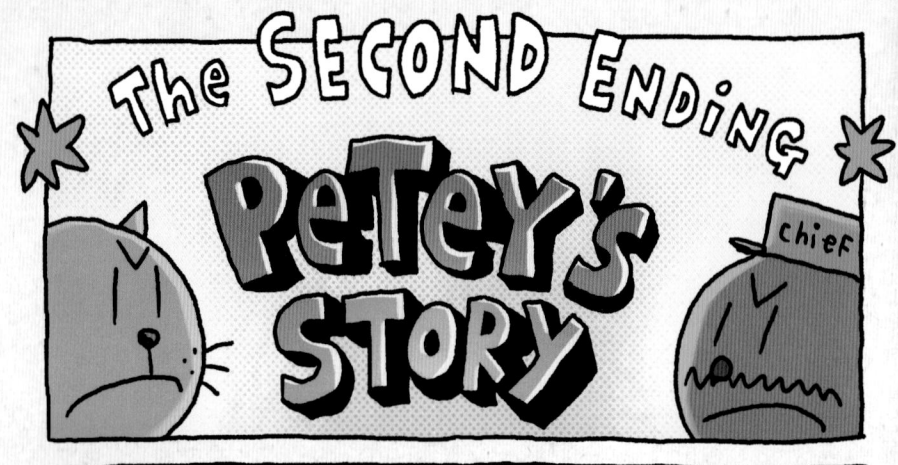

The SECOND ENDING
PETEY'S STORY

Meanwhile, back in the Present...

ALRight, Petey! I'm taking you to Jail!

Why? What'd I do???

You escaped on page 27, remember?

Oh, yeah.

WeLL, kid, it looks Like you'll be staying with Dog Man for a while.

Ok.

You know, Chief, I've gotta change my ways!!!

Yep.

cat jail →

I mean, I've got a kid now!

I Know!

I can't be goin' around being a Jerk all the Time!

That's Right!

I've gotta be **RESPONSIBLE!!!**

I Agree!

I've gotta be a **ROLE MODEL!!!**

So true!

I've gotta be **GOOD!!!**

ABSOLUTELY!!!

Hey Look! Here's his other Flip-Flop!

It took forever, but we finally got all of the pieces!

Have a
happy dream!

and so.....

Good night, 80-HD!

We'll
play
together
Tomorrow!

...if you thought
our adventure
was over...

You Ain't Read NOThin' Yet!

At this very moment, George and
Harold are busy creating their
NEXT work of depth and maturity.

Take a peep,
my peeps!

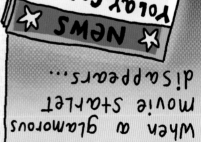

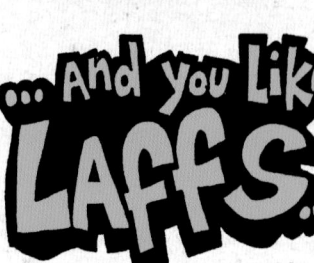

236

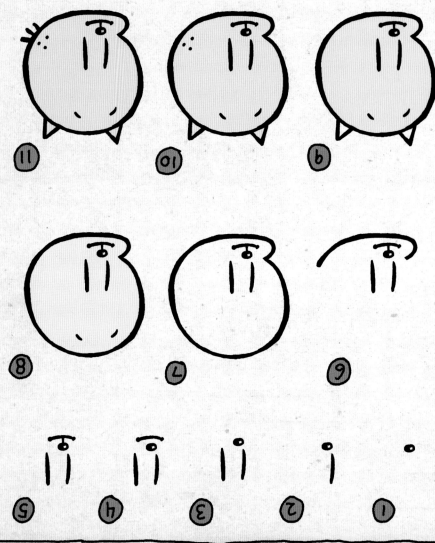

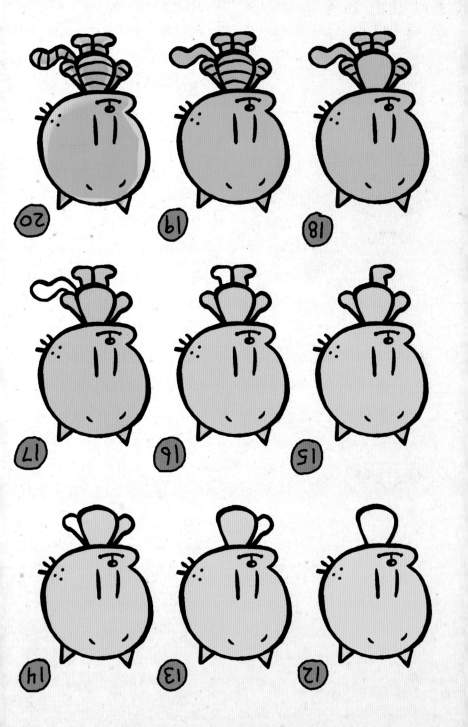

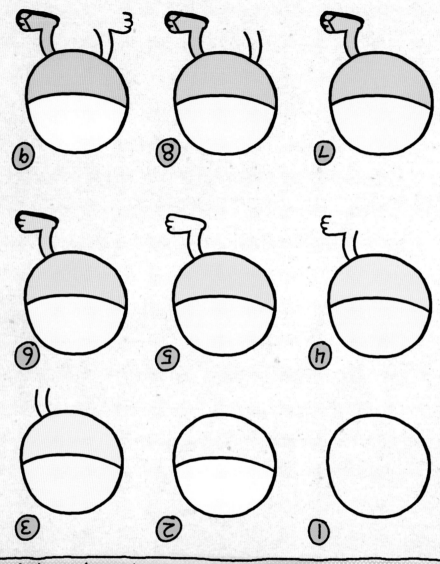

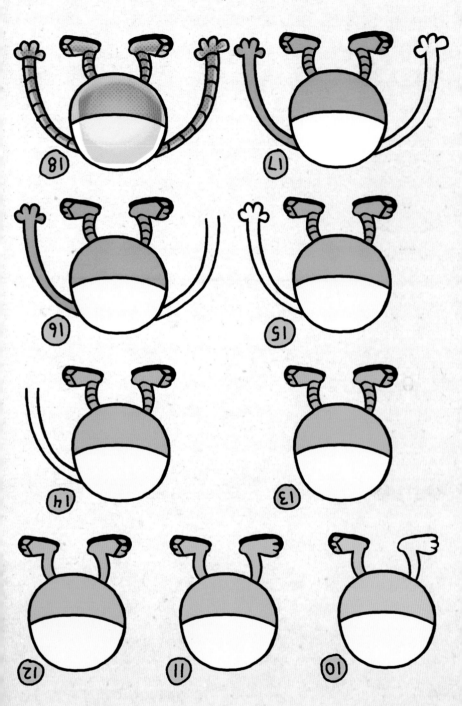

HOW2 DRAW
A BEASTY BUiLDiNG

in 21 Ridiculously easy steps!

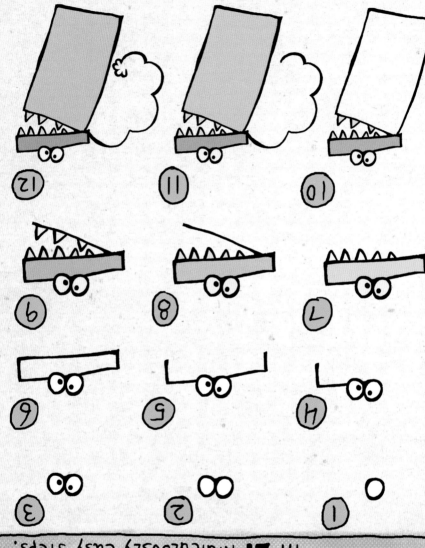

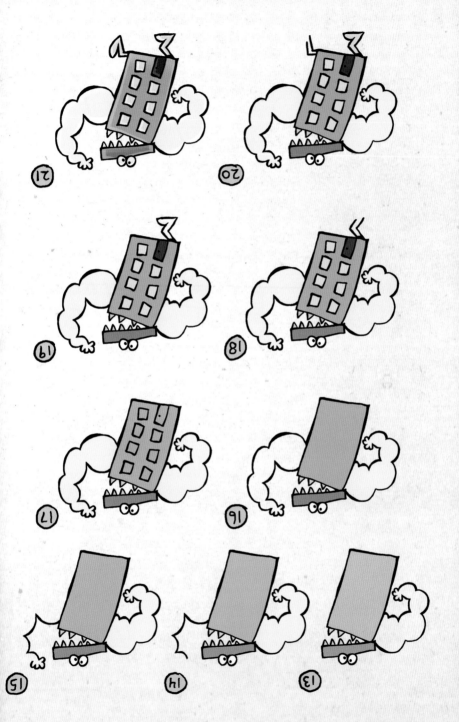

HOW 2
DRAW

HOW 2 DRAW

PeTeY

in 27 Ridiculously easy steps!

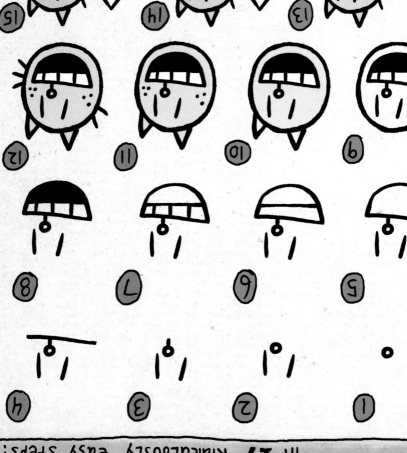

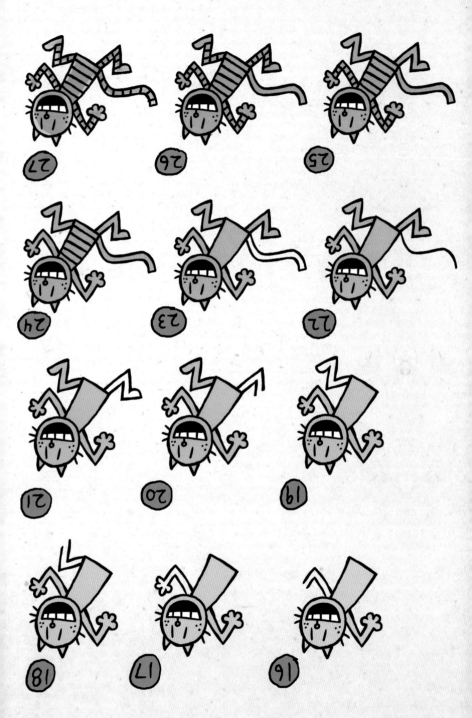

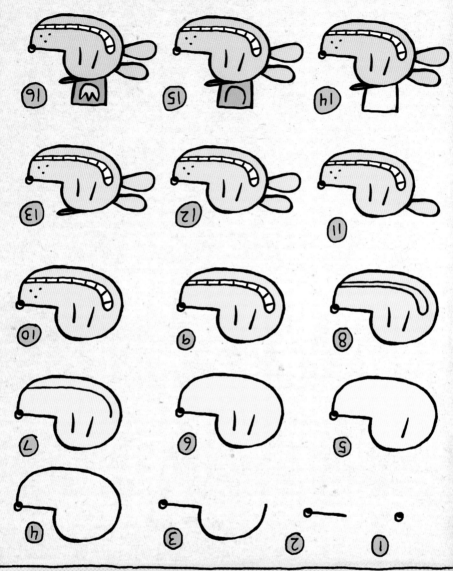

LEARN 2 DRAW MORE
CHARACTERS

at SCHOLASTIC.com and
PILKEY.COM

READ TO YOUR DOG, MAN!

Hey, man! I love to read, man!!!

me too, man!

But did you know there's a way to take your reading "skillz" to the **NEXT LEVEL?**

How, man?

Just read to your dog, man!

Researchers have studied the benefits of reading out loud to dogs.

* University of California–Davis: Reading to Rover, 2010

Reading to dogs has also been linked to increased empathy and kindness.

But what if ya don't have a dog, man?

Check with your local library or animal shelter!

They might have volunteer dogs you can read to!

So take your reading to the next level, man...

... And read to your dog, man!

READING TO YOUR DOG IS ALWAYS A PAWS-ITIVE EXPERIENCE!

SOPHIE, BRIDGET & JAC

MICHAEL, KADEN, WINSLOW, MILO, GAVIN & SOPHIA

BECKY & REESIE CUP

LUCAS & JACK

JOSH & REESIE CUP

REESIE CUP & AJ

LILY & SALMA

SERENITY & LILY

#ReadToyourdogman

KATIE & REESIE CUP

GABRIEL, JACOB & GIZMO

KATE & BRIDGET

KRAMER & CAMERON

ADAM & REESIE CUP

CHEWIE, KYLE, TYGRA, ALEK & PEE WEE

LEARN MORE AT
PILKEY.COM!

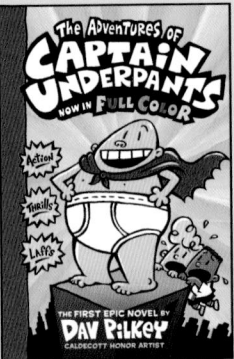

ABOUT THE AUTHOR-ILLUSTRATOR

When Dav Pilkey was a kid, he suffered from ADHD, dyslexia, and behavioral problems. Dav was so disruptive in class that his teachers made him sit out in the hall every day. Luckily, Dav loved to draw and make up stories. He spent his time in the hallway creating his own original comic books.

In the second grade, Dav Pilkey created a comic book about a superhero named Captain Underpants. His teacher ripped it up and told him he couldn't spend the rest of his life making silly books.

Fortunately, Dav was not a very good listener.

ABOUT THE COLORIST

Jose Garibaldi grew up on the South Side of Chicago. As a kid, he was a daydreamer and a doodler, and now it's his full-time job to do both. Jose is a professional illustrator, painter, and cartoonist who has created work for Dark Horse Comics, Disney, Nickelodeon, MAD Magazine, and many more. He lives in Los Angeles, California, with his wife and their cats.